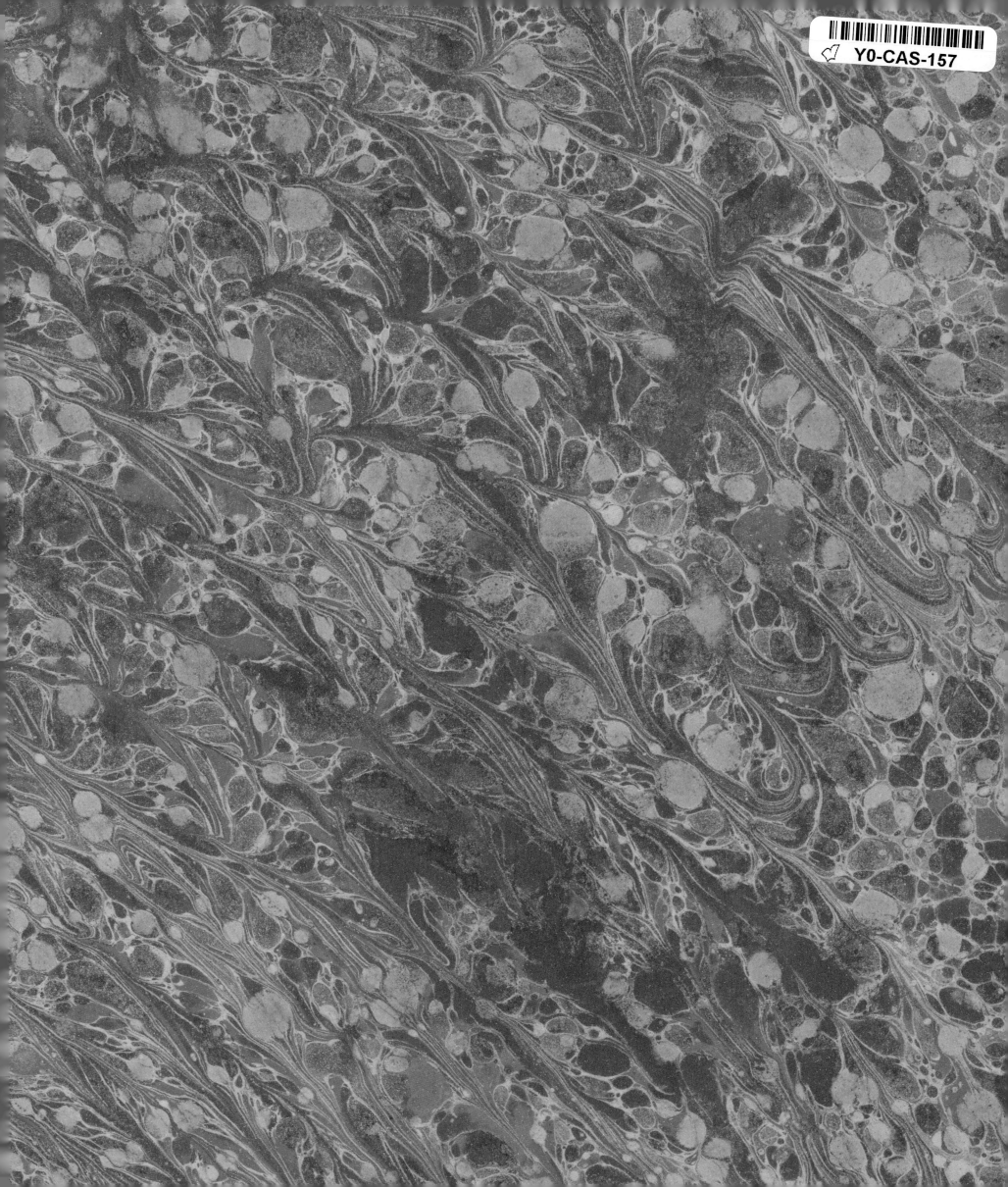

The Unprecedented Discovery

of the

DRAGON ISLANDS

April-June 1819   HMS *Argonaut*

LORD NATHANIEL PARKER R.S.

The Unprecedented Discovery

of the

DRAGON ISLANDS

April-June 1819   HMS Argonaut

Lord Nathaniel Parker R.S.

HAMLYN

THE UNPRECEDENTED DISCOVERY OF THE DRAGON ISLANDS

FOREWORD

This astonishing journal, written in 1819, is the only surviving documentation from a voyage made by one Lord Nathaniel Parker. The extraordinary discoveries that Parker made and recorded in the journal are completely unique. Nowhere else have such plants and animals been found, especially those resembling creatures that have only ever been described in myths. This is what makes the journal so exceptional. Lost for over 150 years, its recent discovery has prompted a closer investigation into the life of this little-known explorer, Nathaniel Parker.

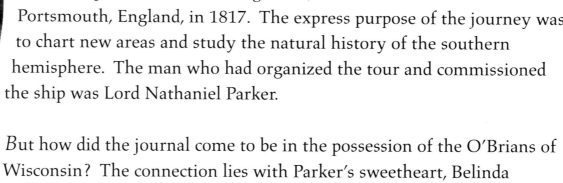

The journal came to light amongst the papers of the late Paul O'Brian, a salesman from Milwaukee, Wisconsin. Paul's family thought the journal a magnificent joke, but were intrigued by the narrator and his enthusiasm. The apparent authenticity of the journal's age encouraged Brad, Paul's nephew, to find out if there was any truth behind the incredible story the book relates. Much to his surprise, he discovered that there had been a ship called the HMS *Argonaut*, which had sailed from Portsmouth, England, in 1817. The express purpose of the journey was to chart new areas and study the natural history of the southern hemisphere. The man who had organized the tour and commissioned the ship was Lord Nathaniel Parker.

The young Belinda Sedgewick, thought to be aged about 25 in this portrait.

But how did the journal come to be in the possession of the O'Brians of Wisconsin? The connection lies with Parker's sweetheart, Belinda Sedgewick, to whom the journal is addressed. Belinda was engaged to Nathaniel before he left and the journal is a personal account of the voyage written just for her. Perhaps she extracted a promise from him to keep a record for her. We know from the journal that Belinda was also interested in the natural sciences, particularly botany, so it was probably for this reason that Nathaniel made such detailed sketches and paintings. It is believed that the journal is only one of an entire series of records that Nathaniel kept and therefore spans a relatively short period of time during the complete circumnavigation.

Drawing of Lord Nathaniel Parker, made by an unknown artist in 1840.

Following extensive research into his family tree, Brad discovered that Belinda and Nathaniel had married but did not have any children. Nathaniel's work, including the journal, was left to Belinda's nephew, Patrick Sedgewick. The journal later passed into the hands of Patrick's daughter, who married an O'Brian, Paul's grandfather. This family emigrated to the United States in 1904.

*A*nd so to Parker himself. He was born in 1790 to the 6th Earl and Countess of Saltmarshe. They were wealthy landowners in the beautiful county of Herefordshire, England. Nathaniel was educated at home by tutors, one of whom had a particular influence on the boy. This tutor, Nicholas Argyll, studied at Oxford and there had formed a friendship with the famous botanist and explorer, Sir Joseph Banks. (There is some possibility that Banks himself would have visited Saltmarshe Manor while Argyll was tutoring Nathaniel.) The young Nathaniel would almost certainly have been inspired by Banks' descriptions of his seafaring adventures with Captain James Cook. Their exploration of the southern hemisphere and discovery of Australia was a major achievement of the time.

Nathaniel's beloved Saltmarshe Manor, the family seat in Herefordshire.

*F*ollowing in Argyll's footsteps, Nathaniel himself went up to Oxford and spent three years there from the age of 18 to 21 studying the classics. However, his overriding interest was always in the natural sciences and, through his hobby, he became familiar with the writings of the Swedish botanist, Carolus Linnaeus and Baron Georges Cuvier, the French naturalist. While at Oxford, Parker had several notable essays published by the Ray Society, of which the most academically renowned was on the sub-class *Cirripedia* (otherwise known as the barnacle).

From the little evidence that has been found about the personal life of Parker, it appears that as a young man he had always been determined to travel and explore the world, but up to the age of 27 had never set foot outside Great Britain. His family completely opposed any such scheme. His father particularly was adamant that he should remain in England and 'not waste fruitless hours chasing wretched butterflies'. It should be said that Nathaniel was an only child and the fear of losing the heir of Saltmarshe Manor would have been great. But the family must have given in to Nathaniel's wishes, as it is recorded

that they paid for the expedition. It seems that Nathaniel managed to obtain his father's blessing in the end.

Portsmouth harbour in the 19th century.

The sloop in which Nathaniel was to circumnavigate the world was the HMS *Argonaut*, recently released from service after the Napoleonic wars. The captain commissioned was Barnaby Ralph, a friend and neighbour to the family and a veteran of the Royal Navy. The officers on board whom Nathaniel particularly mentions in the journal include the ship's doctor Charles Clifton, the captain's younger brother Edwin Ralph, Richard Pearson Fenn, Henry Gilding, and Frederick Heron, all of whom had served with Ralph before. The sloop would have had a crew of between 50 to 70 men.

What follows on the next pages is an exact reproduction of what remains of Nathaniel Parker's journal, recounting the events that took place in April 1819 when the *Argonaut* was washed up on an unknown archipelago in the Pacific Ocean.

April 1st

We are lost. The desperate storms we suffered during the last week (the worst yet) have driven us finally to islands somewhere in the Pacific. The Captain's navigational skills so far have failed him and he, with all his experience, does not recognise our latest harbour. I am assured, however, that it will not be long before he establishes our position and plans our onward journey.

In the meantime the ship must be careened so that damage can be seen to. The bay where we have found shelter, our Salvation Bay, is wide and reasonably shallow. It runs into a beautiful wide beach which itself is surrounded by hills, and volcanic peaks rise further in the distance. Thank God the weather is fine. We have spent the last week continuously wet and at last can dry off. We are fortunate

At times during these torrential storms the boat heeled so that I feared I would never see you again, my dearest. With every crash of every wave, the timbers of the ship shuddered and creaked. The youngest member of the crew, Brett, spent most of his time retching rather than bailing out, poor lad.

The Argonaut limping into Salvation Bay.

Our last known position. I copied this map from the Captain's charts.

South America

It was while painting that I found my ten-legged spider. As you know, all spiders have two body parts and multiple eyes. But a fifth pair of true limbs is exceptional. Many spiders have poisonous fangs with which to kill or stun their prey, but this spider has additional poison glands at the tips of its fifth pair of legs.

Poison gland at end of fifth pair of limbs

Convoluted ducts

Cephalo-thorax

Abdomen

in that we did not lose much from our supplies, and after a brief excursion around the bay, Mr Clifton and I have found that there is an abundance of fresh fruit. Two things of note strike me so far: firstly, we have yet to come across any natives of these isles. If nothing else, they might help us discover our whereabouts. The second is a small curiosity, but significant nonetheless. As I sat painting the view of Salvation Bay, a spider, about an inch in length, crept past me. On closer inspection I realised it had not four, but five pairs of legs! If these islands are as yet undiscovered, what other wonders might I find? Our first expedition is planned for the morrow.

The markings on the spider's body mimic the rocks and foliage of the area in which I found it.

April 2nd

It's been a shocking day, Belinda, and yet (I am ashamed to admit) also intriguing.

At first light the Captain, Mr Clifton, Mr Heron and I with several seamen set off for the peak visible from Salvation Bay. A warm wind from the east blew on our backs as we started our climb. Our aim was to assess our position and scout out areas of interest to explore. After struggling up the hill we reached a high plateau from where the Captain could ascertain our position. We all stood looking north admiring the view when suddenly a terrific roaring filled the air and, unaccountably, flames leapt around us. In horror, I fell to the ground seeing nothing of what attacked us.

On rising, I realised that the Captain was harshly burnt and unconscious. Mr Clifton and I both rushed to his aid, all the time afraid that another attack would happen.

The intrepid explorer

An outline of the island we have landed on — called Parnell's Island, after the seaman that saw it first — and below a view from the top of the ridge heading north.

This was the plateau from where we were attacked.

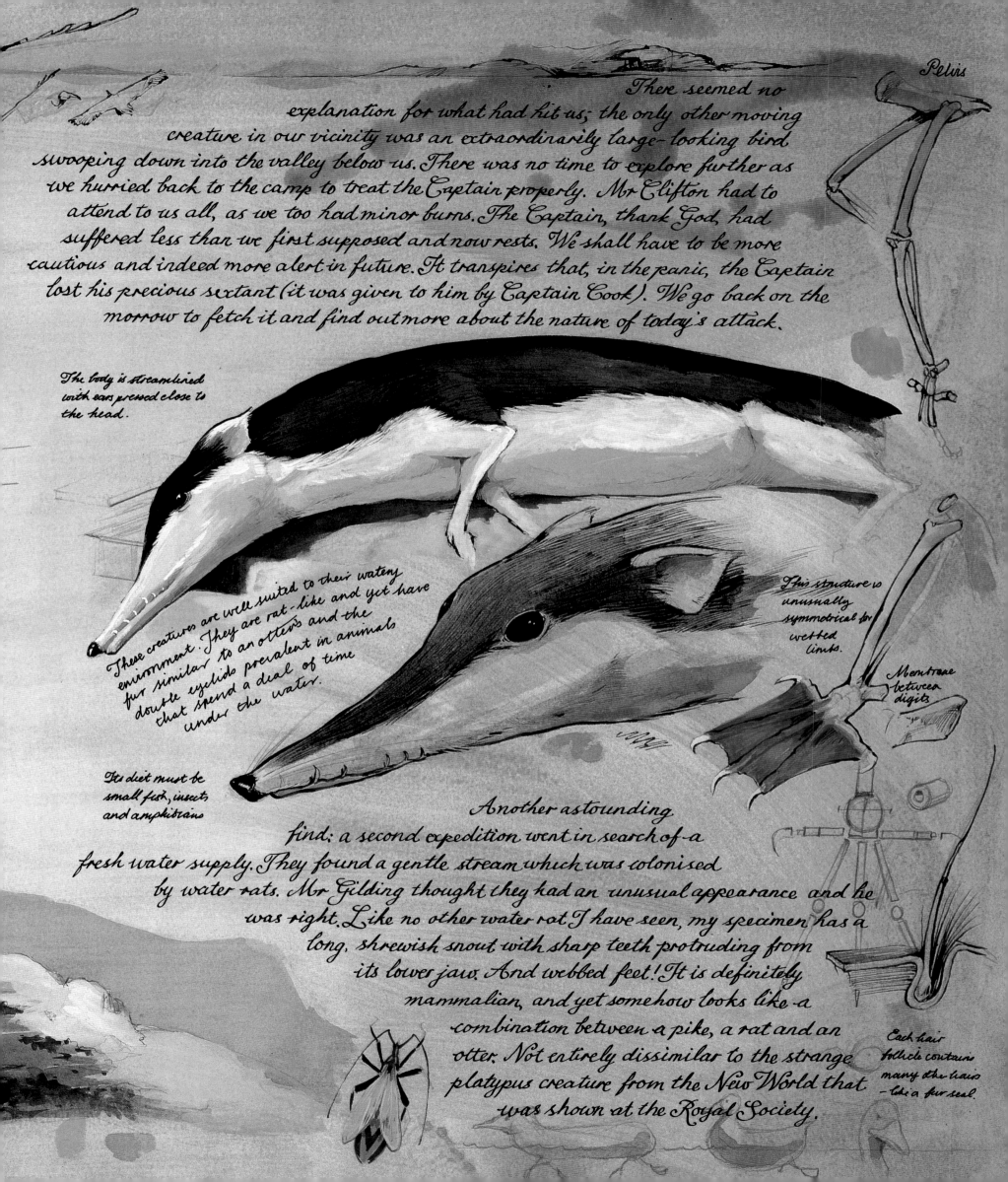

Pelvis

There seemed no explanation for what had hit us; the only other moving creature in our vicinity was an extraordinarily large-looking bird swooping down into the valley below us. There was no time to explore further as we hurried back to the camp to treat the Captain properly. Mr Clifton had to attend to us all, as we too had minor burns. The Captain, thank God, had suffered less than we first supposed and now rests. We shall have to be more cautious and indeed more alert in future. It transpires that, in the panic, the Captain lost his precious sextant (it was given to him by Captain Cook). We go back on the morrow to fetch it and find out more about the nature of today's attack.

The body is streamlined with ears pressed close to the head.

These creatures are well suited to their watery environment. They are rat-like and yet have fur similar to an otter's and the double eyelids prevalent in animals that spend a deal of time under the water.

This structure is unusually symmetrical for webbed limbs.

Membrane between digits

Its diet must be small fish, insects and amphibians

Another astounding find: a second expedition went in search of a fresh water supply. They found a gentle stream which was colonised by water rats. Mr Gilding thought they had an unusual appearance and he was right. Like no other water rat I have seen, my specimen has a long, shrewish snout with sharp teeth protruding from its lower jaw. And webbed feet! It is definitely mammalian, and yet somehow looks like a combination between a pike, a rat and an otter. Not entirely dissimilar to the strange platypus creature from the New World that was shown at the Royal Society.

Each hair follicle contains many other hairs - like a fur seal.

Setting up base camp at the foot of the hill not far from Salvation Bay.

April 3rd

I was frustrated in my desire to set off early as most of the men were needed to haul the Argonaut onto the beach. So I employed my time painting the scene, desperately trying to contain my impatience. The old tub has a damaged bowsprit and several tears in her hull. Mr Heron told me that, depending on what woods were available, there should be few problems and that we'd be away within two weeks.

At last, at noon, five of us got away, heading speedily back towards the peak. Splitting up, we thought we would have a better chance of recovering the sextant. A mile on I heard a couple of musket shots coming from our right. We rushed towards the alarm to find Seaman Kelly trying to drag O'Keefe out from one of the most

The indignity of the ship pulled ashore - rather like the inelegance of a swan out of water.

Parnell's island

The bowsprit should go here

Hull

camp

Salvation Bay

odorous plants I have ever come across. To my nose, the plant smelt of my most favourite food, pheasant casserole, while to every other man it smelt of the most delicious morsel he had ever tasted. (To Seaman Martyn it was ship's biscuits, which I can promise you, Belinda, are revolting!) Once we had freed O'Keefe, we found him to be badly scratched and semi-conscious. Mr Gilding and Kelly took him back to camp, while Martyn and I investigated the plant with care. Digging around the base revealed a bulb from which grew sturdy roots. The bulb was filled with liquid (I have now tested this and found it to be some kind of corrosive). The fantastic smell is emitted by the

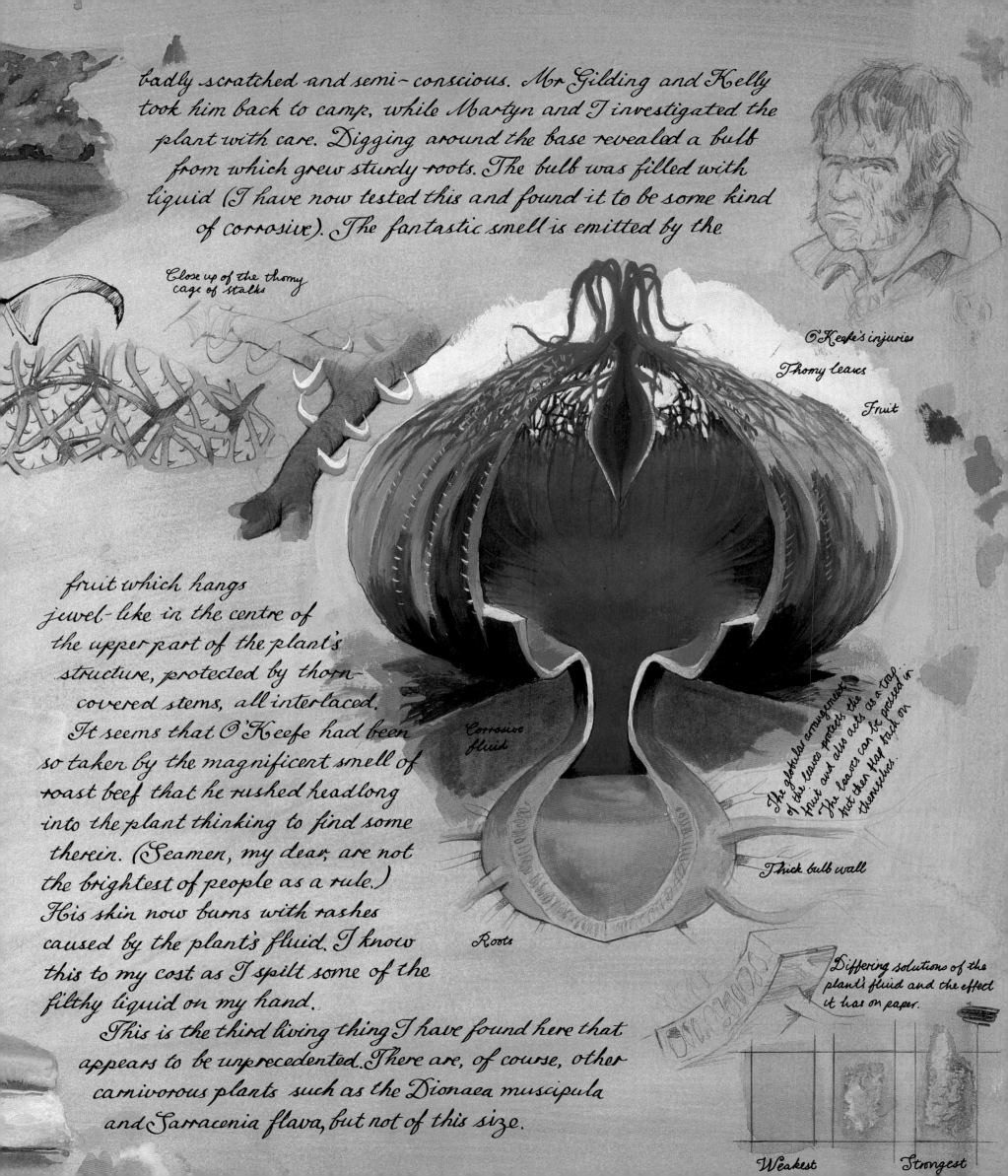

Close up of the thorny cage of stalks

O'Keefe's injuries

Thorny leaves

Fruit

fruit which hangs jewel-like in the centre of the upper part of the plant's structure, protected by thorn-covered stems, all interlaced.

It seems that O'Keefe had been so taken by the magnificent smell of roast beef that he rushed headlong into the plant thinking to find some therein. (Seamen, my dear, are not the brightest of people as a rule.) His skin now burns with rashes caused by the plant's fluid. I know this to my cost as I spilt some of the filthy liquid on my hand.

This is the third living thing I have found here that appears to be unprecedented. There are, of course, other carnivorous plants such as the Dionaea muscipula and Sarracenia flava, but not of this size.

Corrosive fluid

The globular arrangement of the leaves protects the fruit and also acts as a trap. The leaves can be pressed in but then flap back on themselves.

Thick bulb wall

Roots

Differing solutions of the plant's fluid and the effect it has on paper.

Weakest   Strongest

Martyn and I have pitched camp for the night under trees a little distance from the plants (we found several others in the vicinity), so as not to be distracted by the smell.

A cut-through of the bulbs reveals large plant cells, presumably producing the fluid that lies inside. The fluid of a mature plant is filled with the rotting corpses of insects and small mammals attracted to the smell and the fruit of the plant.

April 4th, morning

As we wait this morning for Mr Gilding I have time to recount the sounds of last night. Neither of

Germination of the seed

The leaves turn green as the bulb in the root system starts to bulge.

Gathering strength the leaves start to curl inwards as the cavity forms in the root.

The root system with its bulb containing corrosive fluid is almost formed as

the leaves join together and create a canopy for the flower to grow

I know, Belinda, how you love botany, so I have drawn for you details of this carnivorous plant. It certainly is most unusual.

us slept much, spending much of our time fending off mosquitoes and being awoken from brief dozes either by explosive noises rather like miniature cannons being fired, or by the same strange roaring that I heard when on the hill.

I have just discovered that the exploding noises we heard last night came from the plant expelling its hard seed cases. A hard, round case lands 10–15 feet away from the parent, which then starts to die. The seed case splits to reveal several segments, each one being a seed.

After rain the second seed case unwinds.

Cross section of seed

An individual seed

Outer layer of seed case falls away on expulsion.

The clearing, showing where the nest is sited.

Sunset

Mr Gilding and the others met with us at 11 o'clock (good news, both the Captain and Seaman O'Keefe are faring well). We determined to head along the ridge of volcanic peaks northwards, starting at the peak where the sextant was lost. No sign of it at the peak, however, three hours later we came across what can only be described as a nest. Excepting that it is enormous, at least 16 feet in diameter. Its setting is ominous, scorched earth stretching out to one side and a bank scattered with shiny pebbles and rocks to the other. The hollow is filled with deep, soft, warm ash in which nestle eight huge eggs. The eggs are about a foot in length and heavily pitted as though blasted with fire. Tiny pieces flake off easily but I would hazard a guess that the shell is exceptionally thick. And amongst the pebbles in the bank Mr Gilding found the sextant glinting in the brilliant sunshine. I can only conclude that the bird we observed gliding down from us two days before is the maker of this nest. But is the bird really so large? Sixteen feet. It is too much to think about. The men are starting to get restless, talking nervously of fiery monsters. They are surprisingly superstitious. Next it will be dragons!

We stayed the rest of the afternoon, hiding a reasonably safe distance from the nest to see if a parent comes, but to no avail. Pitched camp and will see what night brings.

We did, however, spot large birds circling around an island further north.

Eggs buried in the warm ash.

An overhead view of the nest, showing scorched area of land.

Actual size

This beautiful tiny bird hovers in amongst the leaves of the carnivorous plant — it probably carries pollen from one plant to another.

April 5th, evening

Nothing all night, so started our return to the camp at dawn, taking with us three of the eggs. Travelling back on the west side of the island we passed high above the cove next to Salvation Bay. Martyn spotted what he took to be a whale, half-buried in the sand. We struggled down the rocks to get a closer look and, dear God, it appeared to be a giant sea serpent! It had not been dead for long, perhaps a day, and looks to have been attacked by some creature even larger than itself. (What a thought.)

I can make no guess as to what extent this serpent reached, the remains, however, are around <u>36 feet</u> long. Martyn was not foolish in thinking it a whale; its mouth seems to echo the whale's baleen system of filtering shrimp from the water. One of the seamen went to inform the Captain of our grisly find. On my instructions, the Captain was able to reassure the men that serpents like this, though large, would

The wounds I found on the body of the serpent are consistent with those made by an octopus or squid, only hundreds of times larger.

What I choose to call the baleen of this serpent is remarkably like the whale's system. It is a form of mesh that sieves small aquatic creatures from the water.

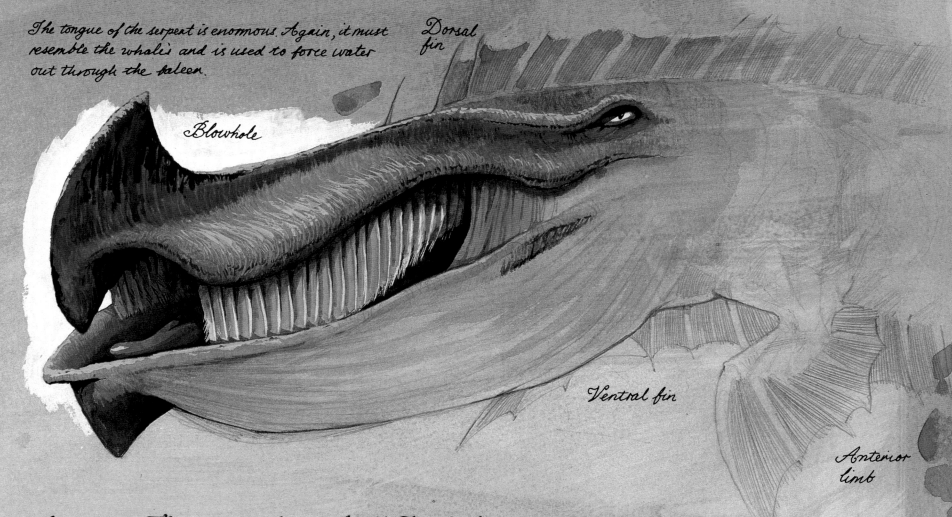

The tongue of the serpent is enormous. Again, it must resemble the whale's and is used to force water out through the baleen.

Dorsal fin

Blowhole

Ventral fin

Anterior limb

not harm us. They can only eat krill. I told him not to mention the animal that most probably killed it. The serpent is covered in circular wounds that have torn its skin and deep gashes that could be bites. It reminds me of an octopus attack and my thoughts are filled with the terrifying myths of the kraken, the giant octopus. I can only hope I am wrong.
Cook felt the meat sufficiently fresh to sample. By all accounts, it tasted of eel, though I did not try it myself. You know, my dear, how I detest eel!

The water around these islands must be teeming with shrimp to sustain a creature this large.

Along the length of the serpent runs both dorsal and ventral fins.

April 7th

Had no opportunity to write yesterday, as you can see I have been otherwise occupied. We're on a longer expedition: sailed north (avoiding the serpent cove) to island from which we would be able to see the peak where the birds were circling. Arrived at dusk and that night witnessed a display of fire in the sky for which I could give no explanation.

Fiery lights accompanied by the strange roaring I have heard several times now.

The dragons do not flap their wings at all, they just glide through the air. At no point do they make any sudden movements, everything seems to happen at a sedate pace.

April 7th

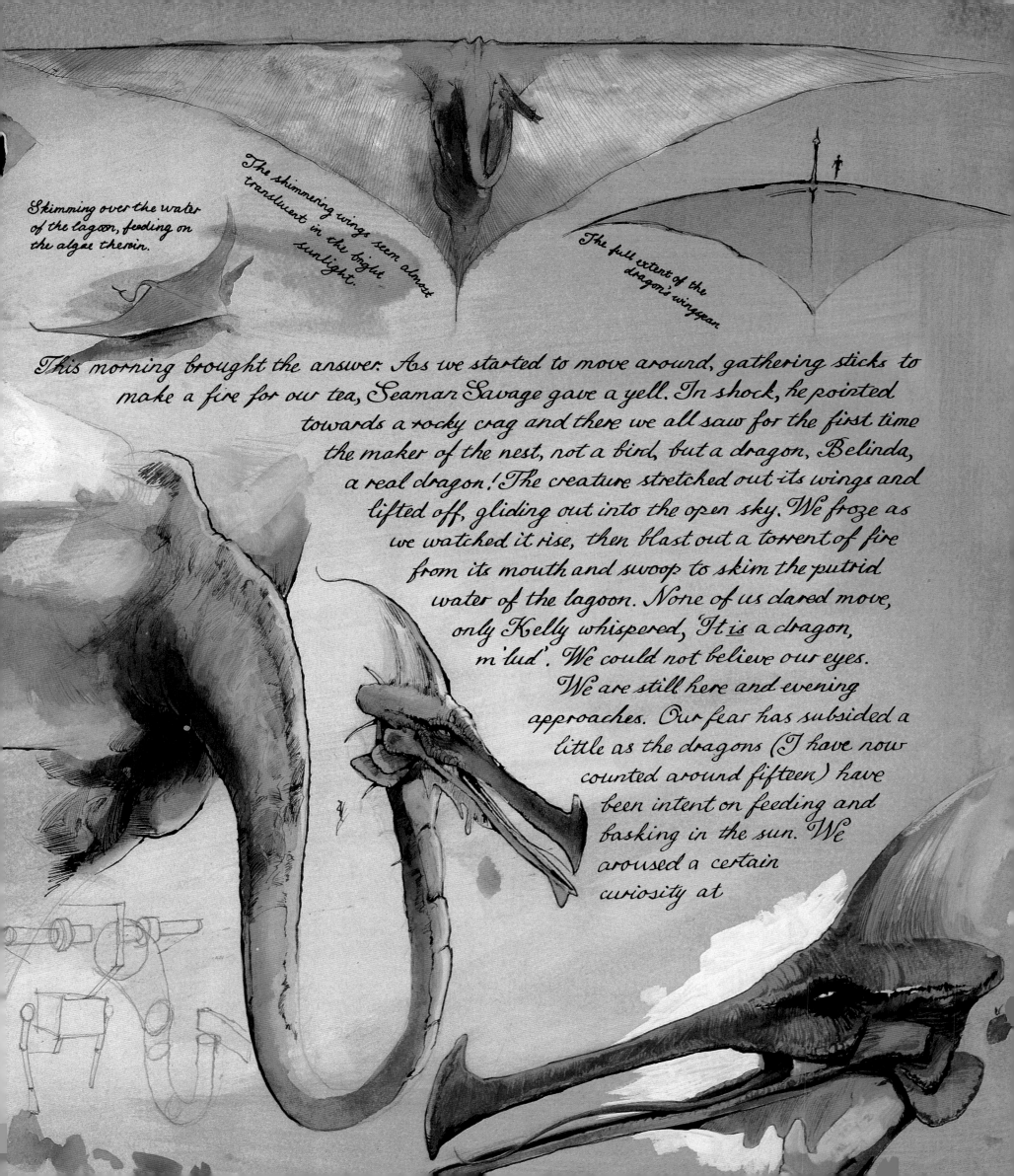

Skimming over the water of the lagoon, feeding on the algae therein.

The shimmering wings seem almost translucent in the bright sunlight.

The full extent of the dragon's wingspan.

This morning brought the answer. As we started to move around, gathering sticks to make a fire for our tea, Seaman Savage gave a yell. In shock, he pointed towards a rocky crag and there we all saw for the first time the maker of the nest, not a bird, but a dragon, Belinda, a real dragon! The creature stretched out its wings and lifted off, gliding out into the open sky. We froze as we watched it rise, then blast out a torrent of fire from its mouth and swoop to skim the putrid water of the lagoon. None of us dared move, only Kelly whispered, 'It _is_ a dragon, m'lud'. We could not believe our eyes.

We are still here and evening approaches. Our fear has subsided a little as the dragons (I have now counted around fifteen) have been intent on feeding and basking in the sun. We aroused a certain curiosity at first but it seems our position makes it difficult for them to approach nearer. (Thank God!) It has been the most remarkable day of my life — to watch creatures you never thought existed, even study their habits! This evening, as they disappear to their resting place, I feel almost affectionately towards them — my dragons. They are not ferocious, indeed they remind me rather of cows, with their bulk and docility. I am forcing the others to stay ~ I feel sure they would all prefer to head back to camp and return with greater numbers of men.

One talent the dragons possess, which all the men have admired, is their grace and ease of movement in the air. The sailors amongst us have watched how they fly and have been able to describe to me how the dragons make the most use of the winds. Savage describes their movements in nautical terms saying that, with their wings outstretched, they appear to 'tack, beat westward and run before'. (I still do not understand these terms, but I take his word for it.) Indeed, Savage said of them 'just like the old Victory herself, 'cepting she never had the luxury of going straight up'.

April 9th

In the last two days I have been studying the dragons intently, but from afar. (You should see the number of books I am filling with sketches.) Today, imagine how I felt when, during an excursion to Dragon's Peak itself, I rounded a promontory and there in a bay lay the body of a male dragon. I could scarcely believe my good fortune. It had probably been there for a couple of days and had been severely burned. But what an opportunity for discovering more about this spectacular creature. Only when so close does one

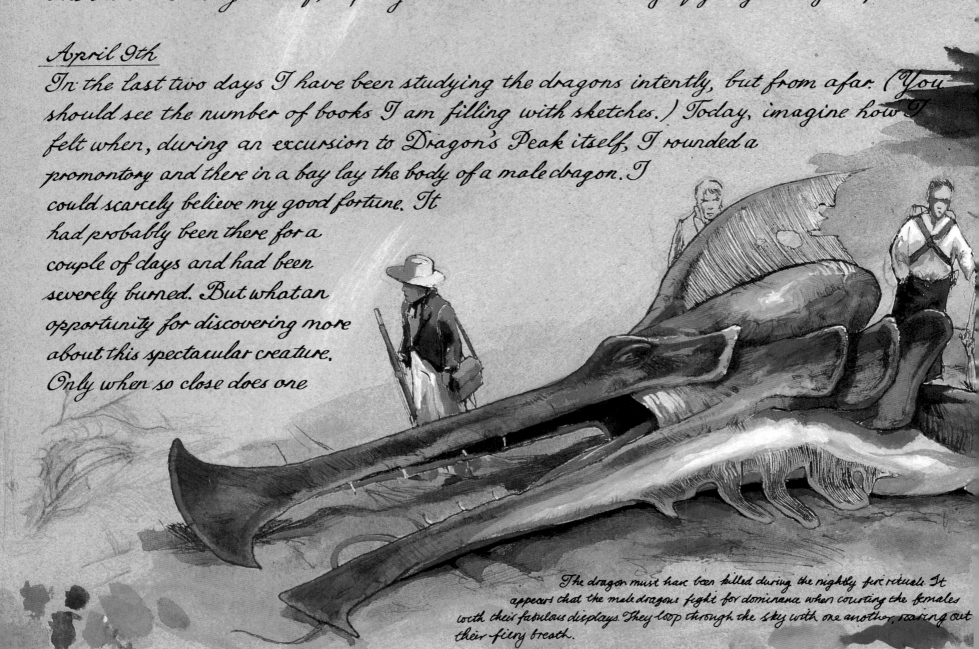

The dragon must have been killed during the nightly fire rituals. It appears that the male dragons fight for dominance when courting the females with their fabulous displays. They loop through the sky with one another, roaring out their fiery breath.

Cross-section
through a wing bone

When examining a piece of the honeycombed bone, I realised to my amazement that it too had a sponge-like framework. A pattern that repeated itself as far as I could investigate with the limited equipment at my disposal. This seemed an ideal combination for both strength and lightness, unsurpassed in Nature.

appreciate how huge the beast is. And the first question that springs to mind is 'How can it fly?'. I decided to start my examination at its head and, as I worked, I marvelled at how light its structure was. One answer lies in its bones – they are not solid, but are honeycombed inside in a way similar to the bones of birds.

The dragon's protuberances, such as its crest and the gill-type flaps on either side of its head, are flexible and built mainly from cartilage. Its body, when compared to those creatures flying above us, had shrunk considerably in volume and its skin lay in folds. Rather similar to a balloon that has lost its air. I conclude that the bulk of a dragon's body is filled with air (or some gaseous substance lighter than air) again making its whole lighter than anticipated. It would make sense, too, that the gas filling its body is flammable – hence the fiery belching. In order to test this theory, I had to puncture one of the corpse's

This drawing illustrates the weight-saving features of the skull – it is pared down to the bare minimum required for structural support.

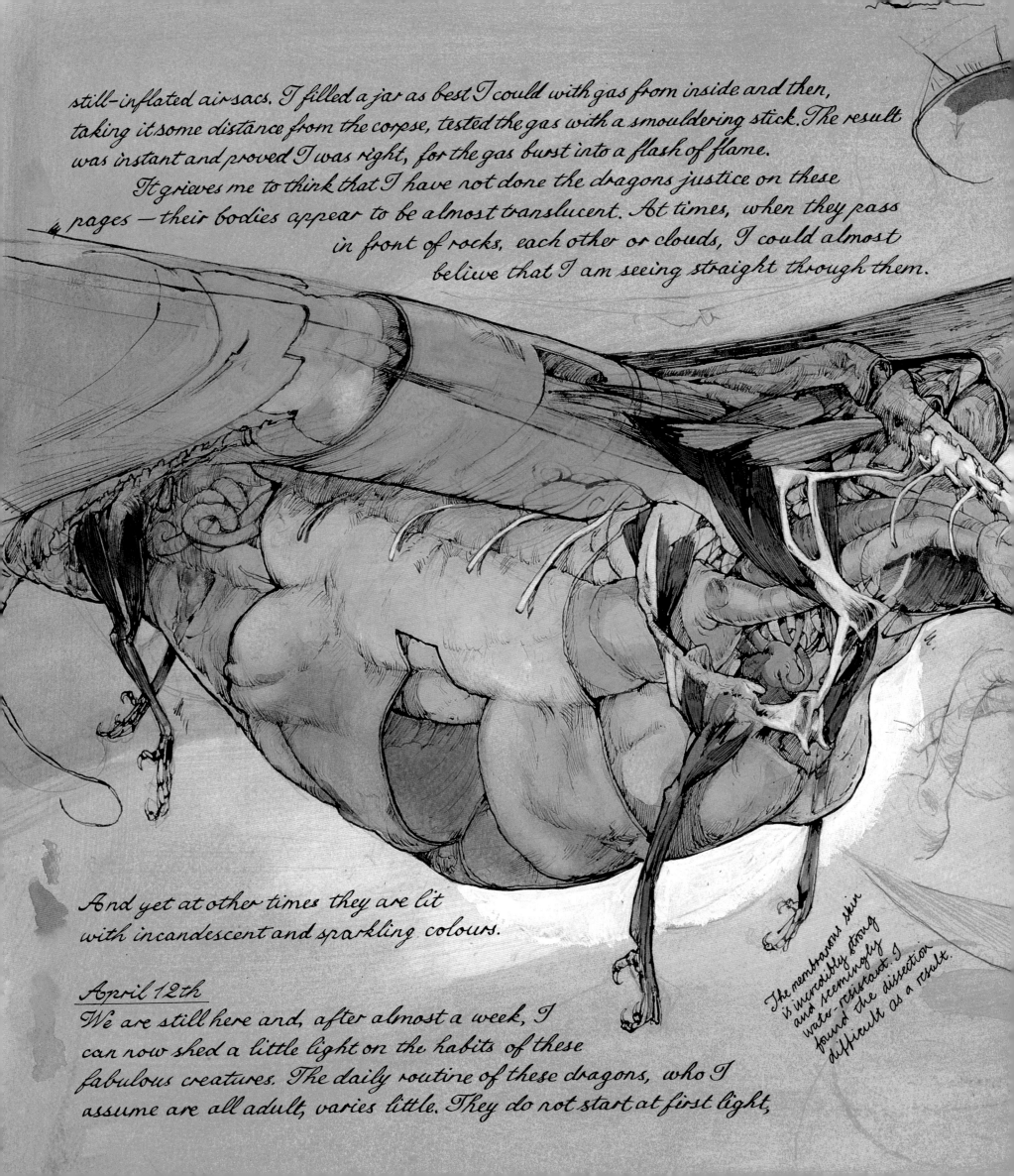

still-inflated airsacs. I filled a jar as best I could with gas from inside and then, taking it some distance from the corpse, tested the gas with a smouldering stick. The result was instant and proved I was right, for the gas burst into a flash of flame.

It grieves me to think that I have not done the dragons justice on these pages — their bodies appear to be almost translucent. At times, when they pass in front of rocks, each other or clouds, I could almost believe that I am seeing straight through them.

And yet at other times they are lit with incandescent and sparkling colours.

April 12th
We are still here and, after almost a week, I can now shed a little light on the habits of these fabulous creatures. The daily routine of these dragons, who I assume are all adult, varies little. They do not start at first light,

The membranous skin is incredibly strong and seemingly water-resistant. I found the dissection difficult as a result.

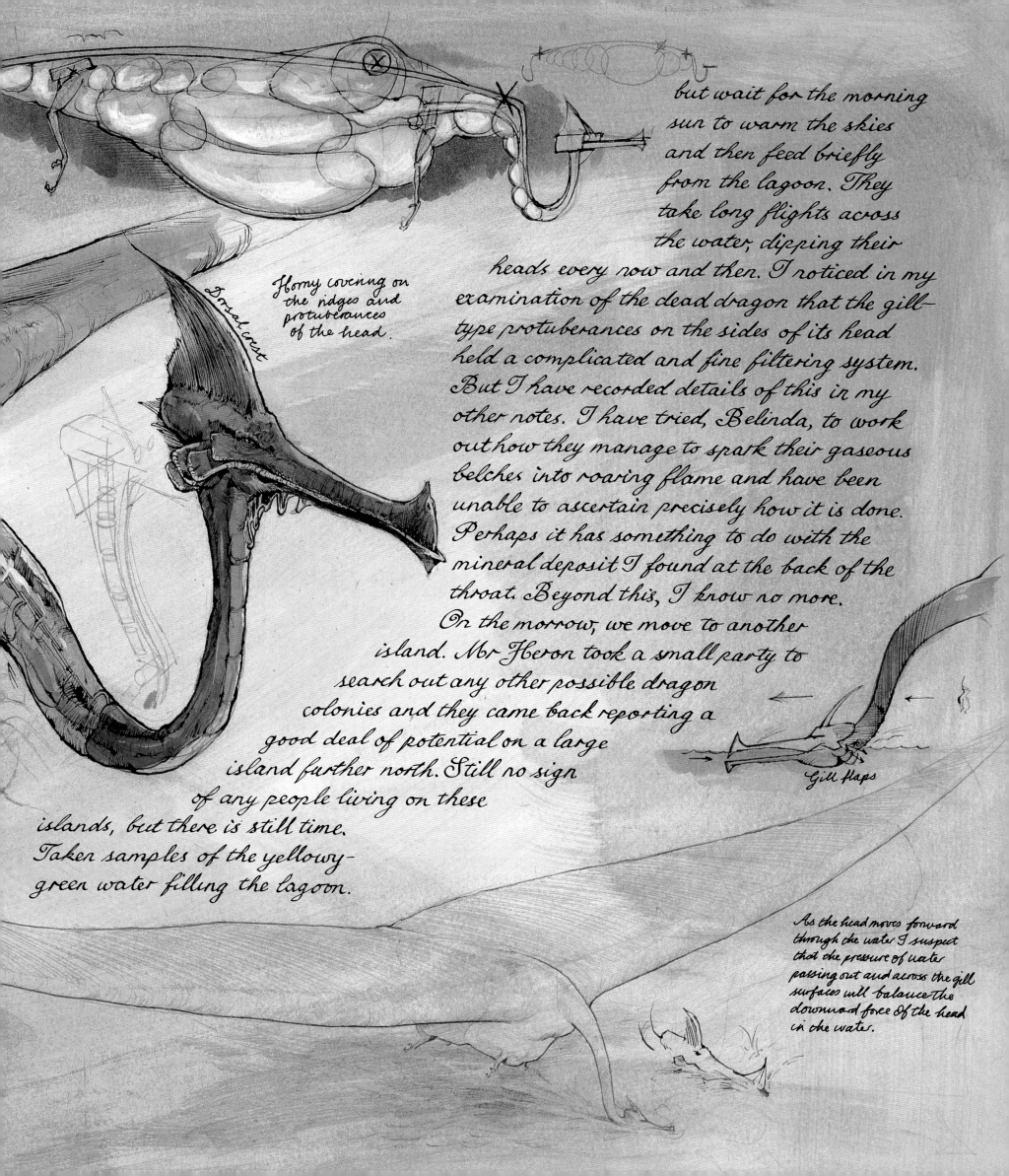

but wait for the morning
sun to warm the skies
and then feed briefly
from the lagoon. They
take long flights across
the water, dipping their
heads every now and then. I noticed in my
examination of the dead dragon that the gill-
type protuberances on the sides of its head
held a complicated and fine filtering system.
But I have recorded details of this in my
other notes. I have tried, Belinda, to work
out how they manage to spark their gaseous
belches into roaring flame and have been
unable to ascertain precisely how it is done.
Perhaps it has something to do with the
mineral deposit I found at the back of the
throat. Beyond this, I know no more.
On the morrow, we move to another
island. Mr Heron took a small party to
search out any other possible dragon
colonies and they came back reporting a
good deal of potential on a large
island further north. Still no sign
of any people living on these
islands, but there is still time.
Taken samples of the yellowy-
green water filling the lagoon.

Horny covering on
the ridges and
protuberances
of the head.

Dorsal crest

Gill flaps

As the head moves forward
through the water I suspect
that the pressure of water
passing out and across the gill
surfaces will balance the
downward force of the head
in the water.

April 12th, evening

Mr Heron has brought us this evening to the island north of the peak. We beached the cutter and climbed the cliffs to pitch camp. At the top, the lazy evening light revealed below us a wide grassy plain. In the distance, we thought we could see more

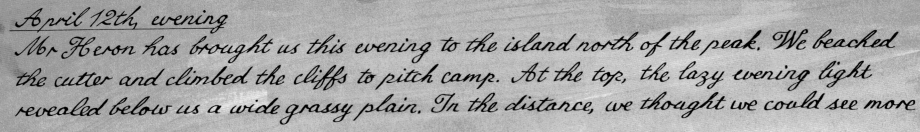

Mr Heron and I looking out from the cliffs across the plain.

dragons circling over a dense forest. We cross the plain and head there on the morrow.

April 13th

We were nearing the forest, when suddenly the air was filled with ear-splitting screeches and dark menacing shapes dived towards us. We dropped to the ground to avoid being slashed by the sharp claws of the ferocious beasts, but to our horror the creatures simply landed and, circling our band with their wings outstretched, they stalked towards us, hissing and

Cliff

Landfall

Our route through Dragon's Peak

As with the dragon, the griffin is remarkably light for its size, though its wingspan measures close to 15 feet. It seems to weigh no more than a Great Dane.

Kelly

Tricknell

spitting. They were horrifying. One of the seamen, in his fright, tried to run for it and was struck down. Thank God Mr Pearson Fenn had the wit to discharge a musket at the leading beast. I followed and, with their leader dead, the attackers took to the air.

We are now in reasonable safety under the trees. We were foolish to assume that the large flying

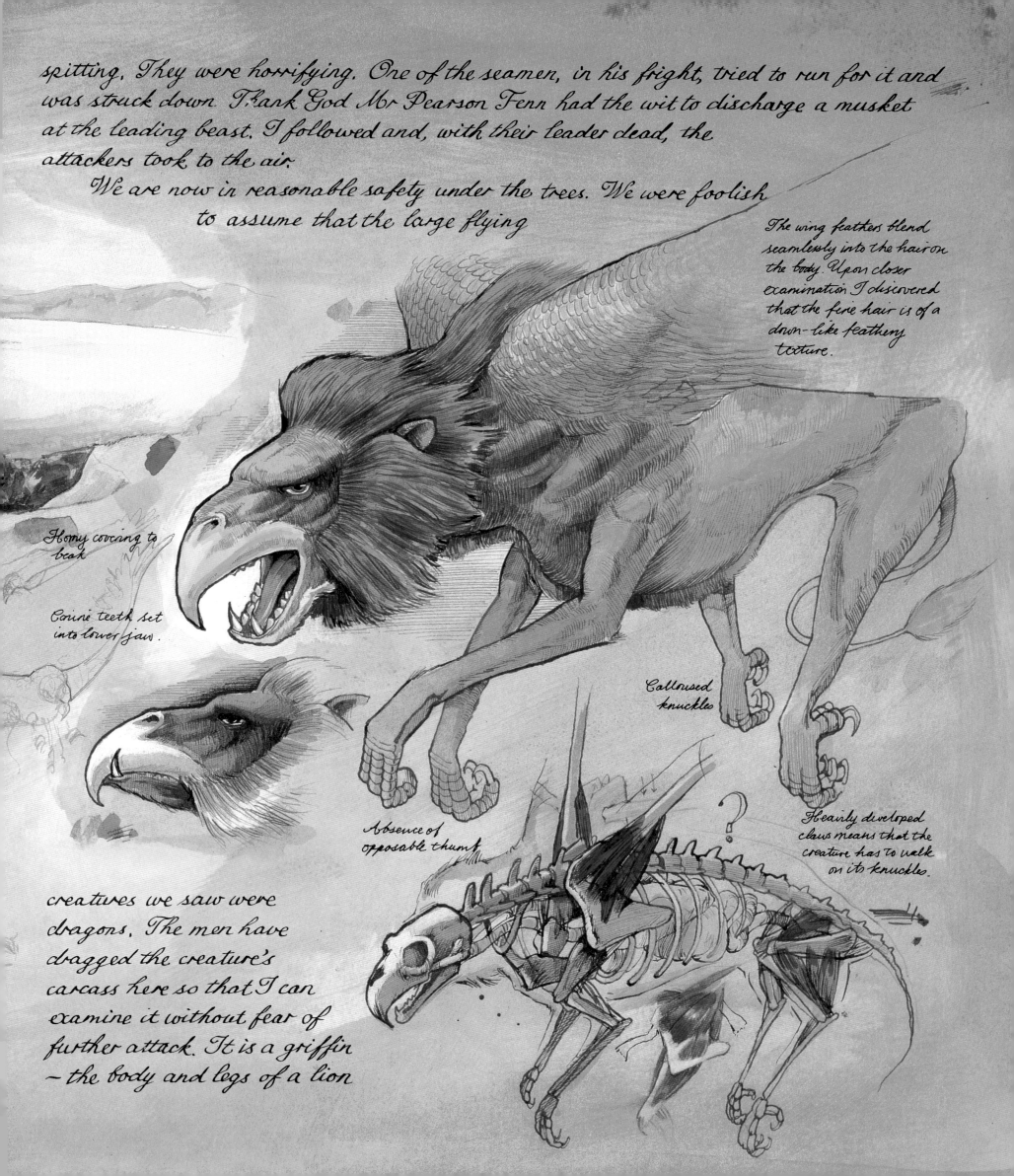

The wing feathers blend seamlessly into the hair on the body. Upon closer examination I discovered that the fine hair is of a down-like feathery texture.

Horny covering to beak

Canine teeth set into lower jaw.

Calloused knuckles

Absence of opposable thumb

Heavily developed claws means that the creature has to walk on its knuckles.

creatures we saw were dragons. The men have dragged the creature's carcass here so that I can examine it without fear of further attack. It is a griffin – the body and legs of a lion

with the head and wings of an eagle. It is magnificent. I have only ever seen these creatures before in books and believed them to be purely fantastical.

To entertain the men as we patched up the injured seaman Miller, I told them of the myths of the griffin. They were supposed to be the guardians of hoards of treasure. This has perversely spurred the men on with greater enthusiasm as they now feel that they might be on a treasure hunt.

April 14th

Because of Miller we decided against pressing on through the forest and have pitched camp here. Our departure depends on the progress of the injured man and my own studies. The griffins are an ever-present menace, hanging over us high in the skies. They circle disconcertingly, like gruesome vultures. So far though, they have not tried to repeat their ambush, but we are always watchful.

The edge of the forest provides us with a choice of fruits, some edible, others not. One bush that proliferates in this area bears fruit that holds a powerful narcotic. One of the seamen sampled a few drops and in minutes was fast asleep. Three hours later he was awake and apparently fine. I have decided to administer the same to Miller to spare him pain.

This afternoon, Mr Heron again led an advance party further into the forest. I quietly continued my drawings while they were gone. In a surprisingly short space of time I heard the sound of movement in the forest, and presumed the party had returned. But instead of men, there were giant birds walking through the trees towards me, ranging in height from around six feet to over twelve. My first reaction was to reach for my musket, but none of us had time.

Before we knew it they were in

These thorny beetles dwell on a fruit tree covered with thorns of exactly the same size and colour. I would not have noticed them, except that as I watched the tree, one of the 'thorns' walked a little distance to sink its jaws into a ripe fruit.

amongst us, crashing around our camp, showing no signs of fear or aggression.

When they had decided that we no longer held any fascination for them, they galloped out into the open plain with their feathery skirts flying. They must be too large a prey for the griffins, because no attempt was made to attack them. I presume that these birds are flightless, as their wings were short and creatures that appear to be so solidly built must find it almost impossible to get off the ground.

I have seen birds similar to these before, Belinda, which is why I had no fear. However, I've never seen them quite so large. They were troublesome to the camp, as their great clumsy steps broke up my operating table and I have spent this afternoon trying to piece together the remains of the griffin, to no avail.

At last the first sign of people on this island. Here are some hand-cut stones, which Mr Heron found on his excursion. Though only a fragment, the symbols depict the shape of a soaring dragon, repeated as a motif. This is contained within what I take to be the spokes of a wheel or, perhaps the rays of the sun. Is this evidence of a past civilisation? Or are the creators of these stones still resident? Are we being watched as we stumble through these lands?

The unicorn's horn is more like an antler. Some of the unicorns have broken ones, perhaps the result of another griffin attack.

The return of Mr Heron and his band of men caused a great deal of excitement. The discovery of the stones and the implications of this are the only topics of discussion this evening. Some of us, particularly myself, are very keen to find out more, while others simply feel apprehensive at the thought of the unknown.

April 15th, evening

My sleep was disturbed this morning by a tremendous rumbling coming from the plain. Creeping to the edge of the forest, in fear of what I might face next on these fantastic islands, I saw a great herd of the most joyous creatures galloping by. Unicorns, Belinda, can you believe it? There must have been around a hundred of them. The ones nearest the forest edge spotted us and veered away, skittishly dancing off to join others a little further on. They are truly glorious, dazzlingly white. But not, as the legends say, the size of a horse. They cannot stand more than seven hands high, yet have all the elegance and grace of thoroughbreds. Their horns are not long and straight but wide and curved and, as I discovered, serve a useful purpose.

We wanted to follow the herd, but felt threatened by the presence of griffins circling above. Staying under the trees, we witnessed an attack on the unicorns. As soon as the griffins started to dive, the unicorns being attacked closed ranks, forming a circle with the larger females backed into the group facing out, horns ready to pierce the onslayers. This defence kept the griffins at bay for some time, but the group was too large and a couple of the griffins managed to wound one of their number inside the circle. At this point the unicorns tried to re-form, but it was too late. They fled, leaving the unfortunate victim to be torn to shreds. None of us can really

An even-toed ungulate - it appears to be an artiodactyl.

Our friends returned, bringing their young with them. They must feel at ease in our presence. (I'm not sure we feel so at ease with them!) I have come across this phenomenon before. Creatures that have not been exposed to man show no fear.

appreciate that we were watching a battle taking place between creatures that we never dreamed existed. Unicorns being attacked by griffins.

As Miller was able to walk today, we travelled under the trees (keeping away from the griffins), heading north towards the lake. We pitched camp at the lakeside. A mist had settled over the whole and we could see no further than the water's edge. When we had viewed the lake days earlier from the cliffs, we had seen a tall structure rising from the lake's centre. Only when the mist clears, will we find out what secret the mist shrouds.

I have heard reports of the ostriches in Africa that it is the male bird who raises the young.

April 16th

It was eerily silent all night and we all felt very subdued. We packed up camp without conversation, which is unusual for us. Each man seemed immersed in his own thoughts. For my part, even though every day has brought a new discovery and excitement, I was overwhelmed with homesickness. I thought of you, my dearest, and wondered how I could have left you for such a long period of time. It's as though the lake and its mysteries made me think to the very core of my being. To dwell on those things I hold most dear.

But I must talk of the lake. As the mists rose that morning we saw for the first time the ruins of a tower rising from the centre of the lake. The original building must have been a wondrous sight. What was the mysterious civilisation that had built such a tower and that had been able to live in harmony with the creatures of these isles? What had become of them?

We found no answers to these questions on the banks of the lake and I railed at not being able to get across the water to explore the ruin. However, as we scrambled around the lake's edge we began to notice a pattern emerging. At regular intervals the trees parted and narrow pathways radiated straight out from the lake, until we came to a very wide path which headed

Most of these tablets are too damaged to piece together. These are some of the best-preserved.

The scale of the tower is overwhelming. Its structure appears to be a simple cylinder, though due to its decayed state it is impossible to know how much more elaborate it once was. There are always three or more dragons in the skies above the tower, upon which they perch.

The radial paths heading out from the lake

due north. The sides of the path were walled and, pulling apart the creepers that now cover them, we could see fragments of plasterwork decorated in elaborate relief. We followed the path north and about a mile on came to a circular harbour. This harbour is about two miles inland from the north coast! And what is so astounding is that the watery canal leading to the harbour has been cut through the

How did the makers of the canal manage to cut through the rocks of the high cliffs surrounding the island?

An overhead impression of the route the canal follows from this circular harbour towards the sea.

cliffs that encircle the island. So the last half mile of canal reaching the coastline has sheer sides, rising over 200 feet high.

We had been walking down the east side of the canal and as we came to the cliffs, found a stairway up the hill. At the top was a stonebuilt platform raised from the ground by five tall steps. It gave us a good view of the coastline, so perhaps it was a lookout post.

A pathway headed east over the hills, which led us all the way around the east coast of the island. We have reached the little bay where we beached the cutter and will again pitch camp and set off on the morrow back to the main camp. We have already been away longer than planned and the Captain and other crew will start to worry if we are not back soon. We must come back here, properly equipped, and explore.

A detail of the circular harbour with its seven docks, or bays. This was clearly a thriving community once.

April 18th, evening, back at camp.
We left Unicorn Island
early today. All
of us happy
to be leaving.
On our return this
evening we learned that
the three eggs we had
previously brought back
with us had hatched
just after our

I've called the
dragons Ignispiritus
volucer-winged
fire breathers.

There are three
layers to the egg's
shell.

departure to Dragon's Peak.
Mr Clifton had been there
to attend the 'birth' (I
think it's a while since
he's done any obstetrics).
He made careful
notes of the various

Boney facing
the ship's cat,
Able.

phases of hatching for me. All
three dragon young have so far survived; indeed they
are very popular with the crew. Mr Clifton tells me that they tried
to feed the young with all kinds of morsels and had little success.
The draglings, as everyone calls them now, are in fact quite capable
of feeding themselves on insects, particularly beetles. However, this
has not stopped members of the crew catching

After a couple of weeks, the draglings have started to test out their wings. At this point, we give them a good run and stand back for a laugh.

A third wing—this would have seemed remarkable a mouth ago!

insects for them, which of
course produces a constant source of study for me.
The variety of insect life on these islands is
remarkable, as I discovered early on with my ten-
legged spider.
  I will remain here for the next
    few days to study

Boney

Nosey

George

the draglings. They are quite
different from the adults, feeding
on insects and being unable to fly
or breathe fire as yet.

The draglings have been named by their keeper, Seaman Leigh. The
maddest one is George, the largest beaked one is Nosey and the most
pugnacious, Boney, in honour of our good King, the Duke of
Wellington and Napoleon Bonaparte respectively.

The draglings will have to undergo many changes before they become fully-fledged adults. Currently they show marked differences in so many respects that they almost seem separate creatures. Do these changes happen gradually, or in a butterfly-like metamorphosis?

April 20th

We have had a disastrous night. At around two o'clock this morning I was woken by the earth shaking beneath me — the tremors that the camp has been experiencing are getting increasingly strong and the one last

I stood and watched the fires burn, too late to save my collection.

right caused a fire to break out in the camp. The worst of it is that the fire spread to the place where I store my samples and a proportion of my collection is utterly destroyed. I feel sick, sick with rage. The Captain has been talking of leaving these last few days and I have been desperately trying to dissuade him. He is a philistine – he does not seem to appreciate how deeply significant my findings are. To crown it all, the draglings have disappeared. The fires of last night attracted several male dragons (no doubt thinking there was competition over here) and the draglings must have followed them away from here. It is imperative that we find them or other live samples to take back with us. Otherwise, who would believe us?

I have managed to extract two days from the Captain to find the draglings and for me to replenish my now depleted stock of specimens. In fairness, he has tried to explain that the safety of his crew and ship are of paramount importance to him. If we lose these because of further tremors, then we are lost and so too my work. But two days, Belinda.

How can I replace the materials that I've lost in that time? Some of my samples were found on the island north of Dragon's Peak and it takes two days just to get there.

Mr Ralph and I are off tomorrow at first light.

The tremors have continued throughout the day varying in degrees of strength. We will all take special care tonight making sure that any lanterns are securely fastened.

Mr Ralph, the Captain's younger brother, and the ship's First Officer.

The men are beginning to break up the camp and collect further supplies of food and fresh water before we depart. Fortunately for the Captain, this coincides with the repairs to the ship being completed.

April 21st

Prepare yourself, Belinda, for I have much to tell and it is not for the faint-hearted. This day has been one I would rather forget. The weather has turned and rain fell on us as we set off in the cutter up the west coast. For an hour we did our best to scan the coastline for any sign of the draglings. We all knew it to be a futile task, so I decided to go instead to pick up further samples of the carnivorous plant (most of which I had lost in the fire). On land,

Our little vessel tossed in the stormy sea.

we split into two parties, Mr Ralph leading one to continue the search for the draglings, and I the other, heading east towards the plants. It was when I was carefully digging out a bulb that we heard two distant shots. It took us a while to reach the grisly scene. Seaman Tully lay dead and Mr Ralph had a deep gushing wound across his back. My immediate task was to tend to Mr Ralph and, as I did so, Seaman Yates told me how the incident had arisen. They were all sheltering under a tree when Tully stepped back into this vilest of creatures and was impaled in its fangs. Mr Ralph tried to free him from the creature's vice-like grip and was himself slashed cruelly. The other seamen were frozen to the spot with terror but, thank God, Yates kept his head and was able to shoot the beast, but it was too late for Tully.

The gorgon lies dead. You can see how easy it was to be unaware of its presence in amongst the tree roots. You could stand on top of it and not notice.

The creature's fangs had ripped open Tully's legs and must have released some kind of toxin into his blood. The monster is so prodigiously foreign

Yates described how the beast sprang up when accidentally trodden on by Tully. The action was just like a spring trap.

Fangs

Pelvic spikes

Sharpened ribs protrude through body cavity

Thick band of muscle covering lower abdomen and pelvis, protecting organs.

This creature is obviously incapable of movement over any distance. It must wait to ambush its prey. How does it ever meet a mate? I dread to think that there must be more of them.

and hideous to look at that I cannot begin to describe it in any way satisfactory to myself. The only name that springs to mind is 'gorgon' as, according to myth, this creature was so unspeakably ugly that no man could lay eyes upon it. I wish never to lay eyes upon this evil creature again.

We all hurried back to the ship with Mr Ralph and poor Tully's body. I have to admit that I also ensured the gorgon's body was brought back for further

Every possible extremity ends in a spike or a claw

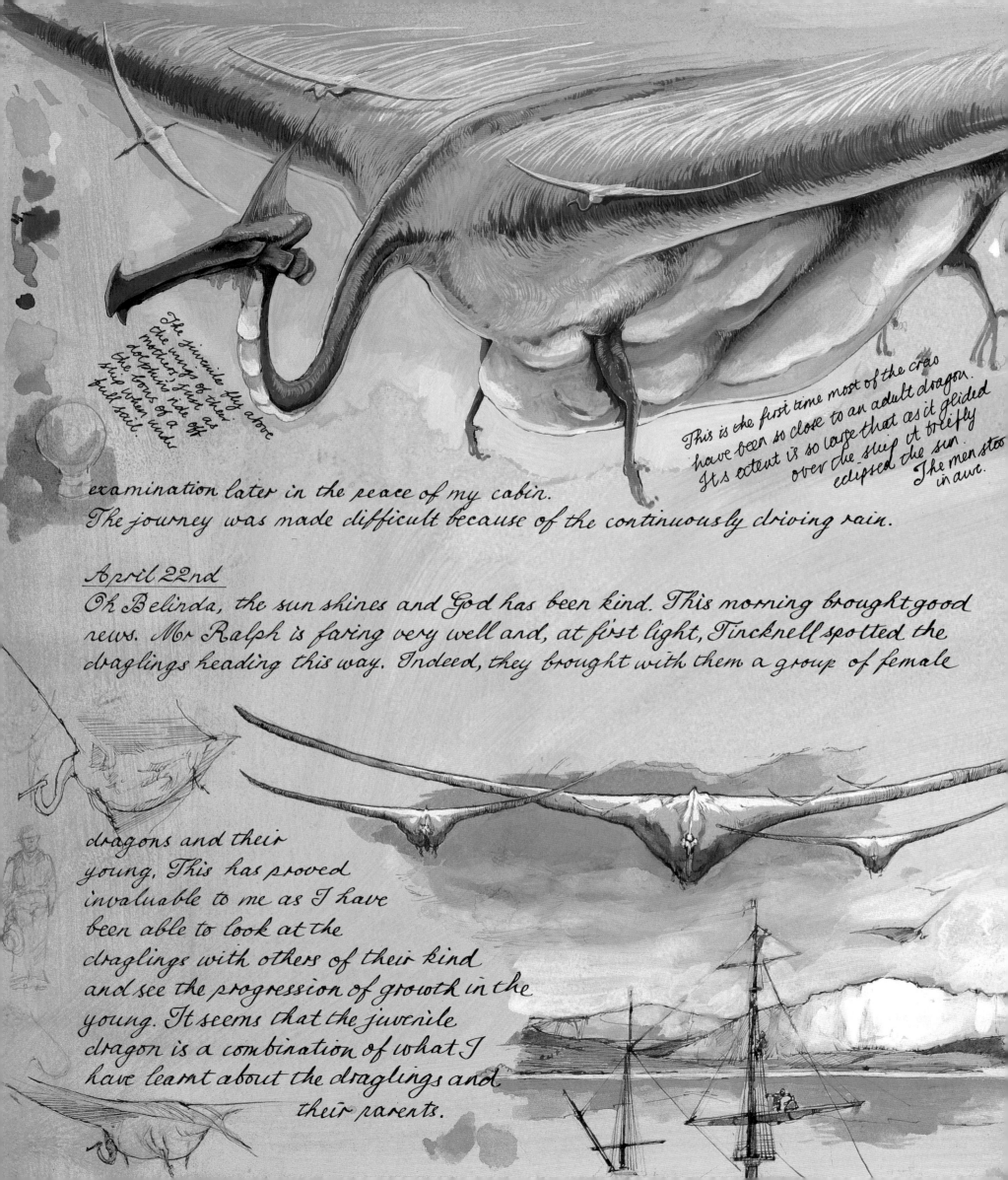

The juvenile fly above the wings of their mothers; just as dolphins ride off the bows of a ship when under full sail.

This is the first time most of the crew have been so close to an adult dragon. Its extent is so large that as it glided over the ship it briefly eclipsed the sun. The men stood in awe.

examination later in the peace of my cabin.
The journey was made difficult because of the continuously driving rain.

April 22nd
Oh Belinda, the sun shines and God has been kind. This morning brought good news. Mr Ralph is faring very well and, at first light, Tincknell spotted the draglings heading this way. Indeed, they brought with them a group of female

dragons and their
young. This has proved
invaluable to me as I have
been able to look at the
draglings with others of their kind
and see the progression of growth in the
young. It seems that the juvenile
dragon is a combination of what I
have learnt about the draglings and
                their parents.

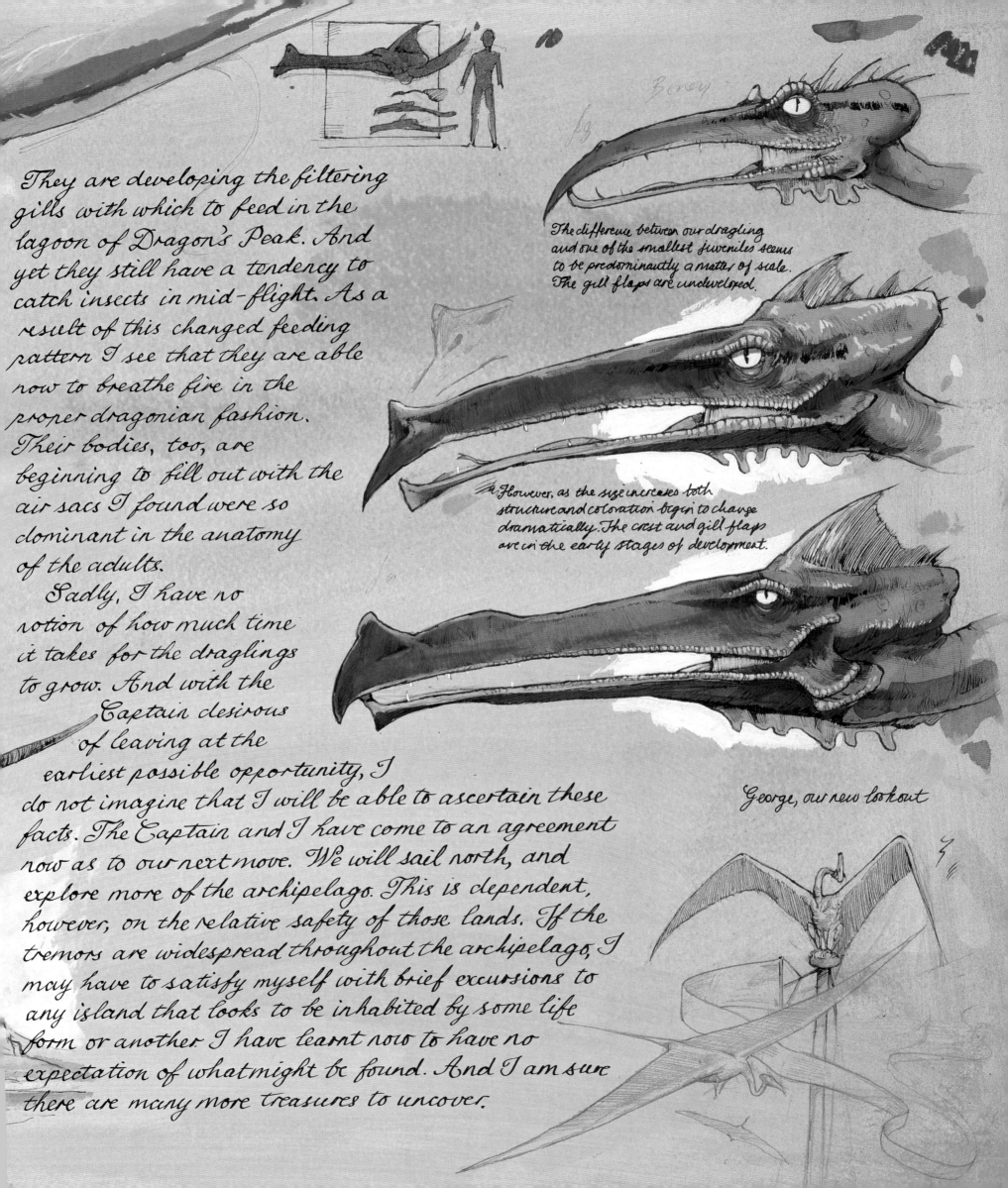

They are developing the filtering gills with which to feed in the lagoon of Dragon's Peak. And yet they still have a tendency to catch insects in mid-flight. As a result of this changed feeding pattern I see that they are able now to breathe fire in the proper dragonian fashion. Their bodies, too, are beginning to fill out with the air sacs I found were so dominant in the anatomy of the adults.

Sadly, I have no notion of how much time it takes for the draglings to grow. And with the Captain desirous of leaving at the earliest possible opportunity, I do not imagine that I will be able to ascertain these facts. The Captain and I have come to an agreement now as to our next move. We will sail north, and explore more of the archipelago. This is dependent, however, on the relative safety of those lands. If the tremors are widespread throughout the archipelago, I may have to satisfy myself with brief excursions to any island that looks to be inhabited by some life form or another. I have learnt now to have no expectation of what might be found. And I am sure there are many more treasures to uncover.

The difference between our dragling and one of the smallest juveniles seems to be predominantly a matter of scale. The gill flaps are undeveloped.

However, as the size increases both structure and coloration begin to change dramatically. The crest and gill flaps are in the early stages of development.

George, our new lookout

Trimming the sails as we heard the relatively safety of Salvation Bay and sail to a new harbour further north.

April 23rd

My fears about the kraken have proved right, Belinda. There was a giant octopus in the waters around the Argonaut. This morning, as we were slowly being towed from Salvation Bay, the ship seemed to run aground. Those rowing in the boat ahead struggled in vain to pull her from what we thought was a sand bank. When the ship started to rock gently, I realised that perhaps this was not the cause after all. When the rocking became more violent and vast tentacles lashed over the side of the deck, spraying water and scattering the men in all directions, we knew without doubt that we were in the grip of the kraken. Mr Heron was the hero of the hour, rounding the men to attack the monstrous encroacher. They managed by their vigorous hacking to release the grip of the kraken. Indeed

I trawled a net over the side of the ship, and on pulling it in, came across two tiny life forms entrapped in the mesh which puzzled me greatly. Many of the creatures I have had the privilege to observe have conformed to some known body plan or design. However, these two creatures, despite their humble size, are in their own way more unique than any of the fantastic flora and fauna I have so far witnessed. I truly cannot classify them.

Mr Heron actually sliced off one of the tentacles. I have successfully matched its sucker markings to those on the sea serpent and can only be grateful that the men did enough damage to the creature to dissuade it from further attack. I would be fascinated to see more of the kraken, but am content to have a tentacle and a floating ship full of unharmed men. There have been several occasions on this trip that have made me fear that I shall never see you and beloved Saltmarshe again and, although I make light of this attack, I had feared the worst. I am not able to reflect on this for long though. The men, on discovering that the kraken's tentacle was simply that of a giant squid, made me promise that they could have it to eat! My examinations have become a race against their appetites.

The kraken's attack has slowed our departure. Thankfully, the boat ahead was not touched by the kraken and they were able to pull us away from danger. However, rigging must be attended to before we can set sail and the hull must be checked again. I told Captain Ralph that it was likely the kraken would have tried to bite the bottom of the ship. No one wants to get into the water to test this theory, however, the side of the hull so far is still watertight.

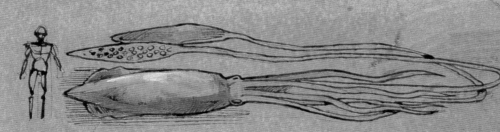

Feasting on the kraken—we all tried it. Even though some were reluctant at first, everyone professed it to be delicious

This friendly little chap and others like him are found in abundance across the islands. He is only 8 inches high.

April 24th

We have been sailing north for the last three hours and already I am feeling nauseous again. I do hope that at some point I will gain my sea legs, but for now I must continue to suffer. The best place for me is on deck. From there I have been able to watch the coastline of the islands we sail past. The Captain keeps an eye out for suitable harbour, but as yet we have found nowhere as accommodating as Salvation Bay.

I have spent some time this morning going through my collection and making further notes. You would not believe, Belinda, how much work I have been able to do. Looking at my research, I cannot help but wonder at the complexities of the natural world. And yet there are also some remarkable coincidences. Take the great flightless birds I have seen. South America has its rheas and New Guinea its cassowaries but now there appears to be a further variation. It is curious that the similarities should be so strong and yet they are each one thousands of miles apart. Now look at these beetles, all found on Parnell's Island. Three of them are almost identical and yet their markings differ in the smallest of details. Our Creator works in mysterious ways, to be sure.

The beetles are only one example of creatures that vary only slightly. More spectacularly, the rat population of the islands is fabulously diverse. Each one suits so entirely its natural habitat. I haven't drawn for you the full variety of the rat-type

Further tablets that were collected from Unicorn Island. I started to record them here simply because the sea air does not seem to preserve them well.

I am intrigued to know what they mean. They remind me of ancient hieroglyphics I have seen reproduced.

creatures found on the islands here either. The water rats with their webbed feet, the pig-like rat with snout and tusks, the flying rat with membranous 'wings', as they alone have filled several sketch books. There are others, too.

My thoughts have also turned to the relief work on the stone walls. Who made them? What do they mean? We are sending Tully to his watery grave this afternoon. I will continue later.

The most exciting thing, as we finished paying our respects to Tully, Brett, who was up in the crow's nest spied something on the horizon. It was a sail. We are making haste to catch up with it. I would dearly love to meet any people who might inhabit these fantastic islands. I go back up to the deck to catch a better view.

Notice the pattern on the sail, Belinda!

We neared the vessel as light was fading and saw it in greater detail. Its sails bore the same markings as those I had found on the walls around the ruined tower.

The most curious thing, just when we thought we might reach them, the ship just disappeared, perhaps it

POSTSCRIPT

The journal ends abruptly here. In the original volume, the last remaining pages are torn out and have never been recovered. It is believed that there were nine journals in total written for Belinda Sedgewick, this probably being the sixth or seventh of the set. As well as this personal diary for Belinda, it appears that Parker also filled a series of books with even more detailed accounts of the flora and fauna he discovered on his two-year journey. These books contained technical and anatomical drawings with scientific notes on the structure, behaviour and habits of the creatures he had observed throughout the voyage. It is a tragedy that these books and the rest of Parker's samples, so painstakingly collected and documented, cannot be examined.

So what of the ship's records? It is not known where the *Argonaut* went after she left the Dragon Islands but it is known that the circumnavigation was, sadly, never completed. HMS *Argonaut* ended her run in the South China seas, shipwrecked just off mainland China. This was a much worse incident than before. Nathaniel was one of the few survivors and, as the others were all seamen, there was no formal or creditable corroboration of events. All ship's records and other notes were lost in the wreck. Only Nathaniel's own story and this journal survives as evidence that this archipelago ever existed.

Parker took his salvaged journal to the Royal Society in 1825 to present his findings to an audience there. To his surprise and horror, he was laughed at and generally abused by the Royal Society members that were present. Unable to accept this, Parker attempted on several occasions to re-present his findings, only to find himself an object of ridicule. Held up to scorn and derision, he eventually became ostracised from society and labelled a raving madman by his peers.

The story of the remaining years of Nathaniel Parker's life is a tragic one. He retreated to a life of seclusion at Saltmarshe, with his wife Belinda as his only companion. Nathaniel remained a recluse, rarely leaving the safety of Saltmarshe, but staying in his study for hours on end, scribbling notes on what was to become something of an obsession - his Dragon Islands. Belinda remained loyal to him throughout the whole period but, sadly, died in her early forties.

So what became of Nathaniel? It seems that he disappeared from Saltmarshe soon afterwards, never to return. Research has shown that another vessel, the HMS *Odyssey*, was chartered by Lord Nathaniel Parker from Portsmouth in 1840. That ship was never to be seen again.

Was Lord Nathaniel Parker a 'raving madman' or had he really stumbled across a hidden environment where creatures previously thought of as the stuff of mythology actually existed? Or was the whole thing an elaborate hoax perpetrated by Parker himself? He even stated that he had met the natives of these islands but by this time nobody would listen to his wild claims. Parker was held up by the establishment as an example to all budding theorists who might attempt to put across new ideas and discoveries.

What evidence we have here cannot prove the existence of these lands and their creatures, but nor can it disprove the possibility that animals and plants such as he describes may have walked the earth. We leave that judgement for you.

GLOSSARY

This glossary contains four categories of words. Firstly, there are the sailing terms and words that are used throughout the journal. Secondly, there are words that are familiar to today's reader but had a slightly different meaning in the early 19th century. Thirdly, there are the mythological names used to describe the creatures found, and lastly, any other words from the journal which might be unfamiliar.

algae: name of a group of plants that live in water, for example, seaweed.

ambush (to): to lie in wait in order to make a surprise attack.

analogue: a word or object which is similar to another or resembles something else. In biology, parts of the body or organs are analogous to each other when they perform a similar function.

anterior: situated to the front, before or earlier in time.

aquatic: of the water.

archipelago: a group of small islands.

artiodactyl: a hoofed mammal with an even number of toes (2 or 4), such as sheep, deer and goats. (See *ungulate.*)

baleen: comb-like plates inside a whale's mouth that sieve krill, or shrimp, from the waters. Baleen is also known as whalebone.

bask (to): to lie in the sun gathering warmth.

beach (to): to haul a boat up onto the beach.

beat westwards (to): a sailing term, meaning to move to and fro across the wind, or tack, heading in a westerly direction. (See *tack.*)

bowsprit: a strong spar, or mast, that sticks out over the front, or bow, of the ship. In a sloop, the bowsprit juts out from the foredeck and acts as a support for the jib sails.

carcass: the dead body of an animal.

careen (to): to haul a ship from the water and expose her underside for repair.

carnivorous: a carnivorous plant or animal feeds on flesh rather than on plants or nutrients from the earth.

cartilage: the substance in an animal's body that acts as a flexible bone. The end of one's nose is made from cartilage.

classify (to): to arrange into groups or classes. This began for the first time in the 18th century when Carolus Linnaeus, the Swedish botanist, started his classification of both the animal and plant kingdom. (See *Linnaeus.*)

colony: a number of people, animals or plants living or growing together.

conjecture (to): to guess.

convoluted: rolled together tightly, twisted together.

Cook, Captain James: a great 18th century explorer. He made three voyages to the southern hemisphere between the years 1768 and 1776, discovering New Zealand and Australia. He was killed in 1779 on the island of Hawaii, after a quarrel with the islanders.

corrosive: having the power to eat away by degrees. Acid is a corrosive as it burns certain substances away.

cutter: a small swift vessel with one mast and sharp bows (sides) that cut through the water, hence its name. It is carried on the ship and lowered into the water when only a few members of the crew explore an area further.

Cuvier, Baron Georges: the French zoologist and geologist. Much of his work involved comparing the structures of different plants and animals.

deplete: to empty or reduce. To have depleted stores means they have been lessened.

diameter: the measurement through or across, in this case, a circle.

Dionaea muscipula: the Latin name for the plant usually known as the Venus fly trap, which feeds on insects by trapping and digesting them.

dissection: the act of cutting into pieces an animal or plant in order to find out more about its inner structure.

diverse: of different kinds.

docility: a creature that is docile is easily managed or controlled, with a gentle nature.

dorsal: on or near the back.

dragon: a mythical flying lizard. The word originates from an ancient Latin word meaning 'serpent'. No one knows where the myth of the dragon first originated, but dragon stories occur all over the world. Dragons are very important in the Far East. The badge of the Chinese emperor was a dragon and some Japanese gods were shaped like them. In Northern Europe, dragons were sometimes symbols of evil and at other times wise and good. They would often guard treasure or a holy place. When evil, they became a test for heroes to conquer, such as in the story of *St George and the Dragon*. Descriptions of dragons in myths have sometimes sounded similar to those of prehistoric animals. Could there be a possible link between them?

emit (to): to send out, to throw and give out.

encroacher: intruder or trespasser.

extent: in this instance, Nathaniel uses the word 'extent' to mean 'size'.

fantastic: in Nathaniel's day the meaning was much closer to the word 'fantasy' (which it originated from) and described something that was unreal or unbelievable, of dreams or the imagination.

flammable: describing something that will burst into flames easily.

foreign: when describing the creature that attacked Tully and Edwin Ralph, Nathaniel uses this word to mean that it is totally alien to him and unlike anything he has ever seen before.

futile: describing something that is useless or pointless.

gorgon: although Nathaniel calls one of the creatures a gorgon, he is using the name to describe how hideous the beast was. In ancient Greek myths, the gorgons were female monsters of the underworld. They were three sisters (the best known was called Medusa) whose hair was made from snakes. It was believed they could turn men to stone with one look. So the word 'gorgon' was used at this time to describe something particularly horrific.

griffin: a mythical creature from Greek myth with the body and legs of a lion and the wings and head of an eagle. The griffin was supposed to have inhabited the ancient land of Asiatic Scythia (central Asia) and there guarded gold and hidden treasures. Anyone who tried to take the treasures was torn to pieces by these fearsome creatures. Pictures of griffins appear in temples around the world from Greek to Buddhist.

hull: the rounded body that forms the shape of the ship and lies in the water.

incandescent: describes something that is white or glowing with heat, almost luminous.

juvenile: a young animal, not yet fully formed.

keel: the lowest timber of the ship that extends from one end to the other and which supports the whole structure.

kraken: a mythical sea monster, spoken of in old seamen's tales. The kraken is said to be a giant squid that attacks boats.

lagoon: a shallow lake or pond into which the sea flows.

Linnaeus, Carolus: the Swedish botanist and explorer. He began the work of combining and naming animals and plants into groups of similar types. These groups were called 'species'. (See *classify*.)

mammalian: describes a member of the class of animals that suckle their young.

membranous: describes something which is made from a thin, flexible organic material.

metamorphosis: a change of form or shape. Caterpillars metamorphose into butterflies and tadpoles into frogs.

morrow (on the): a term meaning 'tomorrow' in Nathaniel's time.

musket: an 18th century gun which was commonly used by soldiers. To 'discharge' meant to shoot the musket.

narcotic: having the power to produce sleep.

nauseous: feeling sick and likely to vomit.

obstetrics: the science of midwifery, that is, the care of women throughout childbirth and the delivering of babies.

odorous: having a powerful smell, either good or bad.

ominous: foreboding evil, threatening.

onslayers: attackers.

opposable: describing something that acts against or resists something else.

paramount: superior to all other things, most important.

philistine: originally this word described an inhabitant of south-west Palestine (known as Philistia). However, it later became a term of abuse, meaning that someone was uncultured, unrefined and without liberal ideas.

plateau: a wide, flat piece of land in a high position.

prevalent: in this instance it means most common.

prodigious: causing wonder and amazement.

proliferate (to): to increase rapidly in number.

promontory: a high point of land standing out from the coastline.

protruding: sticking out. A protuberance is a part that juts or sticks out from the surrounding area.

putrid: describes something that is rotten, decomposed or ill-smelling.

replenish (to): to refill or replace.

rigging: this refers to the system of ropes on a ship that support the masts and sails.

Royal Society: founded in 1660, the Royal Society was set up to promote scientific thought and enlightenment. The *R.S.* after Nathaniel's name shows that he is a member of this society.

run before (to): a naval term, meaning to sail with the wind behind the sails, which pushes the ship forward. The ship will travel in the same direction as the wind is blowing.

Sarracenia flava: the Latin name for the pitcher plant, another type of insect-eating plant. Insects fall into its vase-shaped receptacle, attracted by the smell.

sea-legs: the ability to walk on a ship's deck when the ship is rolling. Experienced sailors are said to have 'sea-legs', as they are totally used to being on board a ship and tend not to suffer from sea-sickness.

sea serpent: a mythical snake-like creature that lives in the sea. There have been many reported sightings of this beast by seamen throughout history, but particularly in the 17th and 18th centuries.

sextant: an instrument used for measuring angular distances. A sextant is also a sixth of a circle and the instrument is shaped as such.

sloop: the HMS *Argonaut* was a sloop, that is, a wooden-built, squared-rigged ship with two masts, having between 10 to 18 guns.

tack (to): a sailing term, meaning to change the course of a ship by shifting the position of the sails. When ships tack, they move across the wind direction. So, for example, if the wind is blowing westwards, the ship will travel first northwest and then tack to head northeast.

thoroughbred: a breed of racehorse that is of pure breed or stock.

toxin: a poisonous substance.

translucent: shining through, allowing light to pass through, but not transparent.

ungulate: any hoofed animal, such as a horse, rhinoceros or elephant. (See *artiodactyl*.)

unicorn: in European myths, the unicorn has the hind parts of a deer, the tail of a lion and the body and head of a horse. From the horse's head sticks a single straight horn, from which the creature gets its name. Unicorns are associated with purity and innocence.

ventral: of the lower side or abdomen. A ventral fin is on the lower surface of the body.

vicinity: places nearby, the surrounding area or neighbourhood.

Victory, HMS: the great man-of-war that was commanded by Admiral Lord Nelson. He sailed it into the Battle of Trafalgar in 1805 where he defeated both the French and the Spanish navies.

TIMELINE

1760 George III crowned King of Great Britain.

1768-79 Captain James Cook explores the southern hemisphere until his death on the island of Hawaii.

1775-83 American War of Independence.

1776 American Declaration of Independence.

1783 Montgolfier brothers fly in their hot air balloon for the first time.

1790 Lord Nathaniel Parker born, heir to the estate of Saltmarshe.

1792 French Republic founded.

1793 Louis XVI executed.

1799 Napoleon comes to power.

1804 First steam train built in England.

1805 Battle of Trafalgar, where Nelson defeats the French navy, and is killed.

1807 Slave trade abolished in the British Empire.

1807 Pioneering steam boat *Clermont* launched, built by American engineer Robert Fulton.

1815 Napoleon defeated by Duke of Wellington in the Battle of Waterloo.

1817 HMS *Argonaut* sets off on world voyage.

1819 The *Argonaut* is washed up on the Dragon Islands.

1820 George III dies.

1825 Nathaniel presents his findings to the Royal Society.

1827 First photograph taken by the Frenchman Nicéphore Nièpce.

1831 Michael Faraday invents the first electric generator, producing a steady electric current.

1837 Queen Victoria comes to the throne.

1839 Belinda, Countess of Saltmarshe dies.

1840 HMS *Odyssey* chartered by Lord Nathaniel Parker. It never returns.

1844-7 Palm House at the Royal Botanic Gardens of Kew built.

1859 Charles Darwin's *The Origin of Species* published.

Original idea, concept and artwork © 1997 John Kelly
Concept and text © 1997 Kate Scarborough

Acknowledgements
Editor: Amanda Li
Art Director: Anne Sharples
Production Controller: Christine Campbell
Handwritten text: Cathy Tincknell
Additional design: Rebecca Herringshaw

The artist and author would like to thank John Moulder for his support and enthusiasm.
The author dedicates this book with love to Freddie and Minna.

Published in 1997 by Reed Books, Children's Publishing, Michelin House,
81 Fulham Road, London SW3 6RB and Auckland and Melbourne.

ISBN 0 600 58966 8

First edition
10 9 8 7 6 5 4 3 2 1

A CIP catalogue record for this book is available at the British Library.

Printed and bound in Spain.

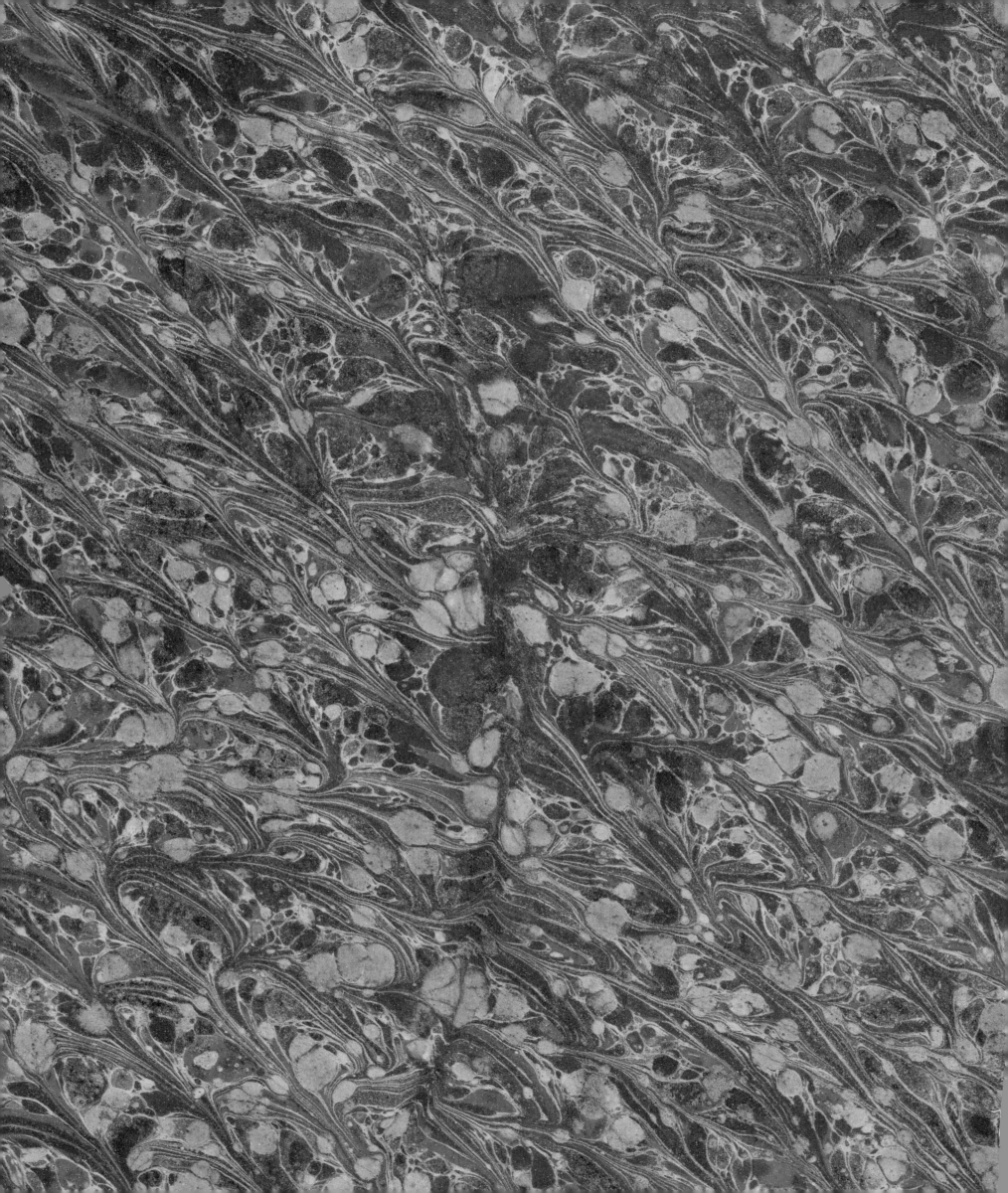